English

The 11+ Practice Book

with Assessment Tests

Ages
8-9

Practise • Prepare • Pass

Everything your child needs for 11+ success

How to use this Practice Book

This book is divided into two parts — themed question practice and assessment tests.
There are answers and detailed explanations in the pull-out answer book.

Themed question practice

- Each page contains practice questions divided by topic. Use these pages to work out your child's strengths and the areas they find tricky. The questions get harder down each page.

Assessment tests

- The second half of the book contains eight assessment tests, each with a comprehension text and a matching set of questions, as well as a set of questions on grammar, spelling and punctuation. They take a similar form to the real test.

- You can print off multiple-choice answer sheets from our website, www.cgplearning.co.uk/11+, so your child can practise taking the tests as if they're sitting the real thing.

- If you want to give your child timed practice, give them a time limit of 30 minutes for each test, and ask them to work as quickly and carefully as they can.

- The tests get harder from 1-8, so don't be surprised if your child finds the later ones more tricky.

- Your child should aim for a mark of around 85% (26 questions correct) in each test. If they score less than this, use their results to work out the areas they need more practice on.

- If they haven't managed to finish the test in time, they need to work on increasing their speed, whereas if they have made a lot of mistakes, they need to work more carefully.

- Keep track of your child's scores using the progress chart on the inside back cover of the book.

Published by CGP

Editors:
Emma Elder, Heather Gregson, Holly Poynton, Jo Sharrock, Camilla Simson

Contributors:
Chloe Buckley, Steve Martin, Julie Moxon, Lucy Towle, Paul Warnes

With thanks to Joe Brazier, Jennifer Underwood and Janet Berkeley for the proofreading.

With thanks to Jane Ellingham for the copyright research.

ISBN: 978 1 84762 840 4

Printed by Elanders Ltd, Newcastle upon Tyne
Clipart from Corel®

Based on the classic CGP style created by Richard Parsons.

CONTENTS

Parts of Speech

Nouns & Pronouns

Underline the word in each sentence which matches the part of speech in brackets. For example:

> I crept up to the hidden <u>door</u> and pulled it open. **(noun)**

1. My cat is extremely old and grumpy. **(noun)**

2. We think that Margot dances beautifully. **(noun)**

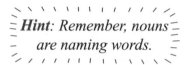
Hint: Remember, nouns are naming words.

3. Caley hasn't told her the top-secret information. **(pronoun)**

4. A green-eyed monster swam slowly past us. **(noun)**

5. The tortoise in the flower bed is ours. **(pronoun)**

6. He really wants to eat at the new restaurant. **(pronoun)**

/ 7

7. The river was fast-flowing and wide. **(noun)**

Nouns

Fill in the gap with the correct collective noun. For example:

> A _____team_____ of **hockey players**.

8. A _____ of **bananas**.

9. A _____ of **birds**.

10. A _____ of **bees**.

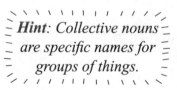
Hint: Collective nouns are specific names for groups of things.

11. A _____ of **cows**.

12. A _____ of **wolves**.

13. A _____ of **lions**.

/ 7

14. A _____ of **fish**.

Parts of Speech

Adjectives & Adverbs

Underline the word in each sentence which matches the part of speech in brackets. For example:

> The judge said that Calvin had a <u>fantastic</u> voice. **(adjective)**

1. Herbert was a famous explorer. **(adjective)**

2. We sprinted quickly past the old haunted house. **(adverb)**

3. A professional chef did a demonstration at school. **(adjective)**

4. Meredith had always wanted a funny clown at her party. **(adjective)**

5. I was trying desperately not to laugh during his speech. **(adverb)**

6. The bride walked confidently down the aisle of the church. **(adverb)**

7. I listened to the teacher as she gave the important instructions. **(adjective)**

/ 7

Adverbs

Underline the best adverb to complete each sentence. For example:

> The baby yawned **(<u>sleepily</u> fiercely)** in its cot.

8. The men danced **(wisely gracefully)** across the stage.

9. Rivers often flow more **(kindly swiftly)** after heavy rain.

10. The fishermen sang **(instantly cheerfully)** all the way home.

11. Leopards are **(closely slowly)** related to lions.

12. The whole class **(obediently badly)** followed the teacher out of the door.

13. Sina marched **(boldly endlessly)** to the cave to face the dragon.

/ 7

14. The chocolate sauce smelt **(consistently faintly)** of garlic.

Verbs

Verbs

Underline the verb in each sentence. For example:

> I <u>finished</u> my book at school.

1. Harry went to Nottingbury by bus.

2. Lyra loves baked beans with mashed potato.

3. We bought sandwiches from the supermarket.

4. Ashleigh danced from sunset to sunrise.

5. Briony took the last slice of pizza.

6. Alfred snored loudly during the school play.

/ 7

7. After 8 o'clock, I shut the curtains in my bedroom.

Verbs

Underline the correct verb from the brackets to complete each sentence. For example:

> Kristin (play **<u>played</u>**) golf yesterday.

8. Ana **(sang sing)** beautifully in the concert.

9. Monty, our pet hamster, **(escaped escapes)** from his cage last night.

10. When I got home, I **(ate eat)** a delicious sandwich.

11. I **(want wanted)** to build a snowman because it is snowing.

12. Lucas **(kept keeps)** his P.E. kit in his locker until it went mouldy.

13. Geraint **(hung hang)** his coat on the peg by the door.

/ 7

14. Michelle **(had have)** never been abroad before the French exchange trip.

Verbs

Verbs

Write the verb in brackets in the past tense. For example:

> Mo **(give)** ____gave____ Katie a birthday present.

1. Minna ran away from the dog that **(race)** _____ towards her.

2. Wen **(look)** _____ around the carriage for his dad.

3. Fin **(bring)** _____ his colouring pencils to the art class.

4. Henry **(take)** _____ the bus to work on Wednesday.

5. Paula had made a picnic which they **(eat)** _____ in the park.

6. Mary joined the knitting club and **(make)** _____ a scarf.

7. Gary **(think)** _____ that the Brussels sprouts tasted awful.

Hint: Some words are irregular and several letters may change when they change tense.

/ 7

Verbs

For each sentence, rewrite the verb in bold in the present tense so that the sentence still makes sense. For example:

> I **picked** raspberries in the garden. ____pick____

8. Ibrahim **clapped** to celebrate the victory. _____

9. Mette **wished** that she could wear trousers to school. _____

10. The orange jelly **wobbled** gently on the tray. _____

11. Leon **chose** to join the orchestra. _____

12. Hannah **left** the building by the back staircase. _____

13. I **blew** a huge bubble in the bright sunlight. _____

14. Maria **bought** the tartan trousers. _____

/ 7

Section One — Grammar

Mixed Grammar Questions

Underline the word in each sentence which matches the part of speech in brackets. For example:

> <u>Kyle</u> couldn't believe what he saw. **(proper noun)**

1. When the orange ball rolled towards the river, Callum chased after it. **(adjective)**

2. The mouse stayed very still so that Mary wouldn't spot her. **(proper noun)**

3. When I left the caravan, I could hear someone talking loudly. **(adverb)**

4. The washing machine ruined my favourite jumper. **(adjective)**

/ 5

5. Lucia had been waiting patiently for fifteen minutes. **(adverb)**

6. The bird landed on the branch without a sound. **(verb)**

7. Are you really going to run a marathon on Sunday? **(common noun)**

8. The picture on the wall by the window is mine. **(pronoun)**

9. The diamond ring sparkled in the sunlight. **(verb)**

/ 5

10. Jill carried the frightened child safely through the stream. **(adjective)**

11. Stu had already marked the place where he wanted me to plant the roses. **(adverb)**

12. The policeman had to remind him of the speed limit. **(pronoun)**

13. One day, when I'm older, I want to own a farm. **(adjective)**

14. I was afraid to play the antique piano. **(common noun)**

/ 5

15. The lantern blew out of my hands in the strong wind. **(verb)**

Mixed Grammar Questions

> Underline the correct word from the brackets to complete each sentence. For example:
>
> > I **(sit _sat_ sitting)** very still while he painted my portrait.

Hint: Read the sentence out loud to yourself to help you choose the correct word.

1. We **(works worked working)** really hard to win the dance competition.

2. The certificate **(tears tearing tore)** in half when they both grabbed it.

3. Milena was **(watching watch watches)** the TV when her brother came home.

4. The nurse is **(careful caring careless)** for his patients.

5. Dad **(kind kindly kindness)** offered to drive us home after the party.

/ 5

6. Tola is going to meet **(your yours you)** at the bus station.

7. Gus **(throw threw throws)** the cricket ball the furthest at last year's sports day.

8. The **(bunch team flock)** of sheep were in the middle of the road.

9. The sun was **(shine shone shining)** through the gap in the blinds.

10. Henry's trip to France was **(him his its)** first holiday abroad.

/ 5

11. Ava showed great **(brave bravely bravery)** by rescuing the cat from the tree.

12. Nena had **(run ran runs)** around the park in the morning before work.

13. Geoff whistled **(soft softly softness)** as he cleaned the car.

14. My sister **(has have had)** brown hair before she dyed it purple.

15. Beth **(lights lit light)** the candles in the sitting room yesterday.

/ 5

Section One — Grammar

Starting and Ending Sentences

> Add a question mark (?) or an exclamation mark (!) to the end of each sentence. For example:
>
> I can't believe you saw a dragon   **!**

1. When can we eat the chocolate elephant ____

2. How long did you have to wait for the ferry ____

3. Camilla just did a bungee jump ____

4. You've got a monkey on your head ____

5. You're not going to the beach, are you ____

/ 5

> Each line contains two sentences. Rewrite the sentences separately with the correct punctuation at the start and end of each one. For example:
>
> at home I enjoy canoeing our house is by a river
> <u>At home I enjoy canoeing. Our house is by a river.</u>

6. can you go in the car with Suki we'll phone you when we arrive

_____

_____

/ 4

7. my dad has been bald for years luckily, the hairdresser polishes his head for free

_____

_____

/ 4

8. we're having an Easter egg hunt in the garden what time should it start

_____

_____

/ 4

Commas

Circle the incorrect comma in each sentence. For example:

Don't worry, we've got plent(,)of time.

1. The hedgehog, which was only a baby, had been, in an accident.

2. When the sitting room, fills with light at sunset, it is delightful.

3. Lightning lit up the sky, there was thunder and, heavy rain.

Hint: Try reading the sentences aloud — commas go where you pause.

4. While you're at the butcher's, can you pick up, some pork pies for lunch?

5. When I was little, I couldn't wait, until I was tall enough to go on a roller coaster.

6. The ship, which was heading for Port Arthur, struck rocks, on the way.

/ 7

7. The town, which was miles from the coast, had a stone, lighthouse.

Put a comma into each sentence to separate the two parts of the sentence. For example:

Dad and I went to Animal World, the largest zoo in the world.

8. Before I had my dinner I practised playing the accordion.

9. As we entered the maze Mum lead the way because she'd been there before.

10. I love going to brass band practice although I get nervous before our concerts.

11. Despite the bad weather forecast we took a risk and went for a walk.

12. Once you've mixed in the water stir the dough for five minutes.

13. Even when it's hot outside the rooms in the castle remain cool.

/ 7

14. After you've finished painting don't forget to clean your paintbrushes.

Section Two — Punctuation

Apostrophes

Apostrophes

Underline the correct word from the brackets to complete the sentence. For example:

> (Kellys' <u>Kelly's</u>) team has got through to the semi-finals.

1. **(Wills' Will's)** dog chases him around the garden every day.

2. Kanye and Joe are taking the **(man's mans')** goat to the park.

3. The **(bird's birds')** wing was injured when it hit the window.

4. Kato invited all the **(policemen's policemens')** children to the party.

5. The hockey **(player's players')** lunches were ready after the match.

/ 5

Apostrophes

Rewrite these phrases using apostrophes. For example:

> the food belonging to the lion
> <u>the lion's food</u>

6. the pets belonging to Marc

_____

7. the water belonging to the boys

_____

Hint: Remember, if the word with the apostrophe is plural and ends in 's', the apostrophe goes after the 's'.

8. the gloves belonging to the girl

_____

9. the paws belonging to the wolves

_____

10. the mugs belonging to the women

_____

/ 5

Apostrophes

Rewrite the words in bold in their shortened form using an apostrophe. For example:

Do not tell Katy what her birthday present is. _____Don't_____

1. I **cannot** work out what I'm supposed to do. _____

2. If **you have** seen the play, you'll understand. _____

3. **I would** be delighted if the Queen asked me to tea. _____

4. **They are** happy to listen to the birds singing. _____

5. **We are** going to be late if Dad is only home at six. _____

6. The film about spider wrestling **was not** very good. _____

7. You really **should not** have gone to so much trouble. _____

/ 7

Use either **it's** or **its** to complete each sentence. For example:

_____It's_____ going to be a lovely day.

8. When I let the dog off _____ lead, it went crazy.

9. This milk is so old that _____ gone off.

10. Our tabby cat has lost _____ toy mouse.

11. The school is changing _____ uniform policy so we can wear fancy dress.

12. _____ been a long time since we went to the fair.

13. The café has opened _____ own stall in the market on Saturdays.

14. Kyle says that _____ his turn to empty the dishwasher.

Hint: If 'its' shows that something belongs to someone, it doesn't need an apostrophe.

/ 7

Speech Marks

Underline the words being spoken in each sentence. For example:

"<u>Would you like a cup of tea?</u>" she asked.

1. "I really want a pirate costume," said Noah.

2. "Look Gary, carrots are on offer," said Mrs Chen.

3. Mr Mackenzie shouted, "Get down off that wall!"

Hint: Speech is always written inside speech marks.

4. Auntie Carole asked, "How long will the roadworks go on for?"

5. "I'll have the tomato salad, please," Yottam said to the waiter.

6. "How did you get here?" asked Katherine.

7. "Look! There's a gorilla in the bath!" Jenna exclaimed.

/ 7

Add speech marks to complete each sentence. For example:

" Nobody will ever find out , " he muttered.

8. It's a long shot , said Pete .

9. There must be a way to escape , she whispered .

10. Basha complained , I don't want to play cricket .

11. Jump ! shouted Harish to the lady at the window .

12. I don't believe you , said Miranda .

13. The giant growled , Where's that child ?

14. We all cheered , Come on Red Team !

/ 7

Speech Marks

Each sentence is missing one comma and either a question mark or a full stop. Add the missing punctuation to each sentence. For example:

" I lost five pounds , " said Robin glumly.

1. " My guinea pig ate my homework " said Arusha

2. Mum asked " How did you get so filthy "

3. Sheila muttered " Why can't you be on time "

Hint: If the speech is at the end of the sentence, the full stop or question mark goes before the final speech marks.

4. " I got lost on Frencham Street " I explained

5. Tim whined " You're hogging the best skateboard "

6. " My lucky socks have spaceships on them " said Caleb

/ 6

Rewrite these sentences using the correct punctuation. For example:

Cliff asked why does no-one like me
Cliff asked, "Why does no-one like me?"

7. Lena whispered he didn't know that

_____

/ 5

8. Amit declared that's Joey's little black dog

_____

/ 5

9. Osei asked where has she hidden our presents

_____

/ 5

10. everyone stop right now Martia shouted

_____

/ 5

Mixed Punctuation Questions

Circle the punctuation mistake in each sentence. For example:

I like to spread ⓑutter in a thick layer on my toast.

1. "We've got to get out of the cellar!".

2. Our house, has six floors, twelve bedrooms and a cinema.

3. Can we swim when we get back from charlie's house?

4. "Milly, stop talking,", said Mrs Wu fiercely.

5. The monster had ten legs, blue hair and a Pink tail.

/ 5

Each of these sentences contains one punctuation error. Rewrite the sentence correctly. For example:

All the rabbit's were hiding in the burrow.
All the rabbits were hiding in the burrow.

6. my friend is moving to the Moon.

_____

7. Sophies' car had broken down.

_____

8. Simon was looking forward to a holiday

_____

9. "Where are the goats? asked Jasminder.

_____

10. "Youre the only person who knows."

/ 5

_____

Mixed Punctuation Questions

Each of these sentences is missing one punctuation mark. Add the missing punctuation mark to each of the sentences. For example:

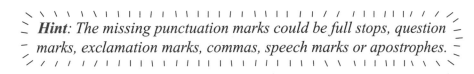

" Please can I go out to play ? " asked Tina.

Hint: The missing punctuation marks could be full stops, question marks, exclamation marks, commas, speech marks or apostrophes.

1. Although rollerblading is Stephen's favourite sport he plays football too .

2. I'm glad its Friday tomorrow as I can't wait for the summer holidays .

3. Hugh often says " Always look on the bright side of life . "

4. Finally it's time to present the prize for Best Film .

5. Why can't we wear skis to school

/ 5

6. My pianos pedals are going rusty .

7. You've done so well and I'm really proud , " said Grandad .

8. My new computer came with speakers a webcam and lots of games .

9. " I can't believe I won ! said Chloe happily .

10. Theyre coming to visit next weekend .

/ 5

11. Although I'm only a child I like reading books about politics .

12. The gala evening raised £2000 for Uppermill Donkey Sanctuary

13. Billy has three hamsters two rabbits and a stick insect .

14. " When are we leaving I don't want to be late . "

15. The lambs fleece was beautifully white in the sunshine .

/ 5

Plurals

Plurals

Underline the correct plural from the brackets to complete the sentence.
For example:

> We keep the sharp (knifes <u>knives</u>) in the top drawer.

1. Two famous (**chefs   cheves**) arrived to judge the cooking competition.

2. We'll divide the cupcake into two (**halves   halfs**).

3. The officers' (**wives   wifes**) were invited to watch the parade.

4. The (**shelves   shelfs**) in the bakery are full of bread.

5. The prize money was divided and stored in two separate (**safes   saves**).

6. Many people feel strongly about their (**believes   beliefs**).

7. I enjoy learning about the (**lifes   lives**) of kings and queens.

/ 7

Plurals

Write the correct plural of the word in brackets. For example:

> We played with all the ____toys____ (**toy**).

8. I believe in _____ (**fairy**) because I saw one in the garden.

9. All the _____ (**boy**) in my class play football at lunchtime.

10. Some _____ (**day**) in winter are very dark and gloomy.

11. There were _____ (**fly**) on the compost heap.

> *Hint: Words which
> end in a consonant
> and 'y' take an 'ies'
> plural ending.*

12. Playing the trombone is one of my _____ (**hobby**).

13. The _____ (**pony**) are running happily around the field.

/ 7

14. _____ (**Daisy**) are my favourite flower.

Homophones

Underline the correct homophone from the brackets to complete each sentence. For example:

> I can't (**fined** <u>**find**</u>) my red shoes.

1. My (**deer** **dear**) son has been studying hard.

2. I'll (**grate** **great**) some cheese for the pizza.

3. I think we'll have (**bred** **bread**) and jam for breakfast.

4. I promised that I (**wood** **would**) lend her my blow-up crocodile.

5. My granny used to work as a (**made** **maid**) at the royal palace.

6. We're going to (**there** **their**) holiday caravan by the sea.

7. Have you (**scene** **seen**) the new Wilkinson Brothers film?

Hint: Homophones are words that sound the same but mean different things.

/ 7

Complete each sentence using **to**, **two** or **too**. For example:

> We're going _____to_____ their house for Christmas.

8. We're going to the shops _____ buy a goldfish.

9. I have _____ brothers called Fred and Jonny.

10. When you go to Paris, can I come _____ ?

11. Carl didn't know how _____ unlock the safe.

12. Mira couldn't drive home because there was _____ much snow.

13. I found _____ kittens curled up next to our fireplace.

/ 7

14. Salil learnt _____ ride his bike in the park.

Prefixes and Suffixes

Underline the word with the correct prefix from the brackets to complete each sentence. For example:

The garage was an (<u>independent</u>   imdependent) business.

1. Another word for naughty is (**disobedient   inobedient**).

2. (**Reheat   Forheat**) the soup, making sure that it's piping hot before you eat it.

3. Mustafa was very (**unkind   diskind**) to me yesterday.

4. Natalie had (**inusually   unusually**) bright green eyes.

5. Mark was talking (**nonsense   unsense**) again.

6. Kayla can be (**unpolite   impolite**) if she's not on her best behaviour.

7. I was (**unable   inable**) to see over the head of the man in front.

/ 7

Add the suffix **ity**, **ion** or **ness** to the word in brackets to complete the sentence. For example:

Chi is the best gymnast because she has good __flexibility__ (**flexible**).

8. Gethin only likes watching _____ (**act**) films.

9. Iftikar sold his stamp _____ (**collect**) at the fair.

10. Sameera noticed the _____ (**similar**) between the sisters.

11. Peering through the _____ (**dark**), I could see a house among the trees.

12. The spider was filled with _____ (**sad**) when he saw he only had seven legs.

13. My dad uses a satellite _____ (**navigate**) system to find his way.

14. I went canoeing at the outdoor _____ (**active**) centre.

Hint: You might need to change the spelling of the word slightly when you add the suffix.

/ 7

Section Three — Spelling

Awkward Spellings

Vowels

For each sentence, add a vowel to spell the word correctly.
For example:

> The eleph__a__nt lived in a big field in the safari park.

1. My brother has started his own comp_____ny selling gadgets.

Hint: Vowels are 'a', 'e', 'i', 'o' and 'u'.

2. The cars were produced in the new fact_____ry.

3. My little brother was miser_____ble when it rained.

4. My mum's friend won £100 on the lott_____ry.

5. Gran gave me a wildlife calend_____r for my birthday.

6. I'll try to d_____scribe what I saw as accurately as I can.

7. Will you defin_____tely have enough time?

/ 7

Consonants

Underline the correct word from the brackets to complete each
sentence. For example:

> The dog **(wagged   waged)** his tail eighty times a minute.

8. He **(waded   wadded)** into the river to catch the fish.

9. I **(triped   tripped)** over and fell into the swimming pool.

10. Naomi had run out of **(wraping   wrapping)** paper so she used newspaper.

11. Carlos couldn't believe he had been **(chossen   chosen)** for the squash team.

12. Marina knew she'd been **(robed   robbed)** when she noticed her purse was missing.

13. Gail was **(riding   ridding)** her scooter when she found the abandoned car.

14. Antonio is **(thiner   thinner)** than the last time I saw him.

/ 7

Mixed Spelling Questions

Underline the correct word to complete each sentence. For example:

Her (**father** farther) likes to be called Papa.

1. I was so (**inpatient** **impatient**) that I couldn't wait for the party.

2. Frank seemed to wear a (**differant** **different**) wig every day.

3. The (**archs** **arches**) in the castle are made of carved stone.

4. The kangaroo didn't pick up on the (**tension** **tention**) in the room.

5. (**Leafs** **Leaves**) turn orange and red in the autumn.

/ 5

6. Mr Herbert is going to take us to pick (**blackberrys** **blackberries**).

7. Juliet had (**written** **writen**) her notes, but they had disappeared.

8. My mum said I could go out if I helped her wash the (**dishs** **dishes**).

9. If you lead an (**inactive** **unactive**) life, you may put on weight.

/ 5

10. Shen started doing (**voluntry** **voluntary**) work when he lost his job.

11. There were lots of (**stories** **storys**) in Dad's book of fairy tales.

12. The mayor (**pinned** **pined**) a gold sticker on the winning entry.

13. I followed the (**pattern** **patern**), but somehow I made a shirt with three sleeves.

14. The library was packed with (**referance** **reference**) books.

/ 5

15. When we were in the jungle, we had to (**purify** **purefy**) water to drink.

Mixed Spelling Questions

Each sentence contains a spelling mistake. Underline the word with the error and write the correct spelling on the line. For example:

Lilly is <u>completley</u> hopeless in the morning.   _completely_

1. What are you smileing about?   _____

2. I missread the instructions and glued my eye shut.   _____

3. The parachute landed at the foot of the cliffes.   _____

4. Don't be a coword Anton, just jump!   _____

5. The birthday cake that Mum made is barely edable.   _____

/ 5

6. Doug is very inportant, so be polite to him.   _____

7. Do me a faver and go to the chemist's on your way.   _____

8. We both left our watchs in the changing rooms.   _____

9. It was suny so our sponsored walk was great.   _____

10. The children took there lunches to the park.   _____

/ 5

11. I couldn't decide which cloths to wear to the disco.   _____

12. The king was the most powerfull man in the land.   _____

13. George was running laps around the boundry.   _____

14. This yoghurt has no flavour; it's totally tastless.   _____

15. The bees were huming loudly inside the hive.   _____

/ 5

Section Three — Spelling

Alliteration and Onomatopoeia

Alliteration

Add a word to each sentence to complete the alliteration shown in bold. For example:

> There was a **p**urple **p**attern on the __pottery__.

1. **S**am **s**at **s**ilently on the _____.

2. The **t**omato **t**astes _____.

Hint: Alliteration is when a sound is repeated at the start of words within a phrase.

3. He **p**oured a **p**int of _____ juice.

4. I **ch**ose the **ch**ips that were _____.

5. **W**endy **w**ore a _____ pair of **w**ellingtons.

6. **B**arry is a **b**ald **b**aker, who likes _____.

/ 7

7. **S**paghetti **s**auce **s**pilt all over the _____.

Onomatopoeia

Underline the onomatopoeic word in each sentence. For example:

> The bee <u>buzzed</u> past my ear.

8. Somewhere in the quiet night, an owl hooted sadly.

9. Rick crashed up the rocky path to the peaceful forest.

Hint: Onomatopoeia is when a word sounds like the noise it describes.

10. The greedy pig gave a low grunt when he saw the farmer.

11. Guy trudged through the bog, his shoes squelching with every step.

12. When Oliver tripped, the silver tray he had been carrying clattered to the floor.

13. The pile of books suddenly fell to the floor with a huge thud.

/ 7

14. Kalena jumped as she heard a key rattling in the rusty lock.

Imagery

Imagery

Each sentence contains a metaphor or a simile. Write down the technique used in each sentence. For example:

The swimmers moved like fish underwater. ___simile___

1. The football pitch was a battlefield. _____

2. The moon was a white dinner plate in the sky. _____

3. His fists were like rocks. _____

Hint: A simile compares one thing to something else. A metaphor says that one thing is something else.

4. My brother is an animal at mealtimes. _____

5. Our kitten is a spoilt princess. _____

6. The scarecrow was as still as a statue. _____

7. Her eyes shone as bright as diamonds. _____

/ 7

Imagery

Complete these similes using a suitable word. For example:

The man was as blind as a _____bat_____.

8. The little girl was as quiet as a _____.

9. On Christmas Day, Granny was as busy as a _____.

10. During the summer, the well was as dry as a _____.

11. The door to the dungeon was as solid as a _____.

12. When Mum is angry, her expression is as cold as _____.

13. The newborn baby was as light as a _____.

14. When she heard the news, she went as white as a _____.

/ 7

Synonyms

Synonyms

Underline the word in each question that has the most similar meaning to the word in bold. For example:

start   slow   stop   <u>begin</u>   fast

1. **mend**   hurt   fix   break   replace

2. **jolly**   satisfied   tired   nervous   happy

3. **concerned** careful   dangerous   worried   excited

4. **sea**   lake   river   ocean   pond

5. **clever**   generous   keen   kind   intelligent

6. **silly**   wrong   wise   foolish   mistaken

7. **glossy**   rough   shiny   peaceful   flat

Hint: Words with very similar meanings are called synonyms.

/ 7

Synonyms

Underline the word from the brackets that has the most similar meaning to the word in bold. For example:

The palace was very **pretty**. (<u>attractive</u> spooky grand)

8. It was getting late and I was starting to feel **tired**. **(bright sleepy old)**

9. Mrs Watson liked to go **jogging** after work. **(cycling swimming running)**

10. Karen hid in the **cupboard** and watched David search. **(stool cabinet table)**

11. Dr Savania was a good doctor because he was **caring**. **(helpful polite kind)**

12. Magnus **jumped** off the creaky diving board into the pool. **(ran leapt climbed)**

13. Timothy **watched** his favourite film again. **(looked viewed tried)**

14. Melanie was **uneasy** about moving to Nepal. **(nervous excited afraid)**

/ 7

Antonyms

Antonyms

Underline the word in each question that has the opposite meaning to the word in bold. For example:

> **hot**   windy   cool   <u>cold</u>   wet

1. **tame**   alive   wild   escaped   home

2. **frowning**   pleased   smiling   angry   bored

3. **elderly**   old   young   aged   active

4. **near**   close   wide   distant   short

5. **old**   clean   expensive   new   scruffy

6. **ill**   poorly   sick   cheerful   healthy

7. **clean**   broken   dirty   natural   perfect

Hint: Words with opposite meanings are called antonyms.

/ 7

Antonyms

Underline the word from the brackets that has the opposite meaning to the word in bold. For example:

> Fabio wondered when the concert would **start**. (**<u>end</u> begin last**)

8. Our next-door neighbour's cat is **bald**. (**ginger soft hairy**)

9. Priya left **early** for her audition. (**late punctually before**)

10. Mick didn't want to **blame** her for what had happened. (**give praise hate**)

11. The idea behind the plan is **simple**, so it should work. (**right complex OK**)

12. My Aunty Sheila has a wide circle of **friends**. (**companions family enemies**)

13. I would really like to **succeed** in my new job. (**win fail bad**)

14. The room looked **appealing**. (**rich familiar disgusting**)

/ 7

Creative Writing

Adjectives

Replace the word in bold with a different adjective which has a stronger meaning. For example:

> The new baby is **small**.   _____tiny_____

1. The play we went to see was **bad**.   _____

2. Aditi packed a **big** suitcase for her holiday.   _____

3. Polar bears live in **cold** conditions.   _____

4. The pink silk dress was **pretty**.   _____

5. We were **pleased** to hear the good news.   _____

6. My great-grandma is **old**.   _____

7. Matteo made a **tasty** pizza.   _____

/ 7

Speech

Each of these sentences contains some speech. Complete each sentence without using the word "said". For example:

> "Put your chairs under your desks," _instructed_ the teacher.

8. "How long will you be in town?" _____ Ariel.

9. "I'll be really well behaved if you bring me a present," _____ Theo.

10. "Perhaps we could go down to the arcade together," _____ Amy.

11. "But I don't want to do my homework," _____ Arthur.

12. "You can't do that!" Krys _____.

13. "Smithson, bring me the map now," _____ the general.

14. "My leg is bleeding," _____ the wounded policeman.

/ 7

Creative Writing

Write two sentences describing each of the following things.
Use adjectives to make your writing interesting. For example:

> What your house looks like:
> My house is semi-detached with a dark blue front door.
> It is built from red bricks and has a sloping roof.

1. What the town or village where you live is like:

_____

_____   / 2

_____

2. What the weather was like yesterday:

_____

_____   / 2

_____

3. What your school is like:

_____

_____   / 2

_____

4. What you did for your last birthday:

_____

_____   / 2

_____

Non-Fiction Writing

You can improve your writing by understanding the purpose of different texts. Write down whether each of these sentences is persuading (P) or informing (I). For example:

> You should try Emma's gingerbread, it's the best in town.   P

Hint: Persuasive writing often uses lots of adjectives to try to appeal to the reader's emotions.

1. Watch Robo-cat, the crime-fighting supercat, on channel 2 this Saturday!   _____

2. Queen Elizabeth I was Queen of England for more than 40 years.   _____

3. Blue whales live in the ocean and are the largest animals on Earth.   _____

4. Try ballroom dancing because it's lots of fun and a great way to stay fit.   _____

5. This Christmas, buy the new Flying Fox which lets you fly to school!   _____

6. In Iceland, the phone book is organised by people's first names.   _____

/ 6

Write a sentence persuading a friend to do each of the following tasks. For example:

> To read your favourite book:
> You must read this book because it has an exciting ending.

7. To come to your birthday party:

_____

_____

/ 2

8. To go for a picnic at the weekend:

_____

_____

/ 2

Non-Fiction Writing

These short passages describe a task in the past tense. Rewrite each passage as a set of instructions in the present tense for someone doing the same task. The first instruction has been done for you.

Hint: Think about how you would tell someone to do something if you were speaking.

1. **Making lemonade:**

   I took three lemons and squeezed them. I stirred sugar into the lemon juice. I poured fizzy water over the lemon and sugar. I mixed the lemonade well. I poured it into a jug and I added a slice of lemon to decorate it.

   Take three lemons and squeeze them.

   _____

   _____

   _____

   _____

   _____

   / 4

2. **Catching the bus:**

   I walked to the bus stop. I waited for bus number 36. I got on the bus and asked for a single ticket to the library. I paid £1.70 and sat down on the bus. I pressed the button to let the bus driver know that I wanted to stop at the library.

   Walk to the bus stop.

   _____

   _____

   _____

   _____

   / 4

Assessment Test 1

This book contains eight assessment tests, which get harder as you work through them to help you improve your English skills.

Allow 30 minutes to do each test and work as quickly and as carefully as you can.

You can print **multiple-choice answer sheets** for these questions from our website — go to www.cgplearning.co.uk/11+. If you'd prefer to answer the questions on the page, just follow the instructions in the question.

> Read this passage carefully and answer the questions that follow.

The Dinosaur Dipper

Sanjay and his dad had been waiting in the queue for the roller coaster for a long time. Bored, Sanjay tugged Dad's sleeve, "Are we nearly at the front?"

When the family had arrived at the theme park that morning they'd bought their tickets from a friendly lady who was dressed as a cavewoman. When they
5   walked through the gates of the theme park, the Dinosaur Dipper roller coaster was the first thing Sanjay had seen. It towered over the other rides, its shiny green track looping high above the ground. Brightly-painted carriages zoomed along the tracks, and the passengers' excited cries echoed through the air.

"Can we go on that ride, Dad?" Sanjay had begged. "Please?"
10   "Be patient," Dad had replied. "We're going to take Maya on some smaller rides first." Maya was Sanjay's baby sister. She was only three, but she was running around and shouting excitedly because she was happy to be out of her pram.

Finally, Dad and Sanjay had left Maya and Mum at the café and made their way towards the Dinosaur Dipper, where they had queued for what seemed like hours.
15   All of a sudden, the queue in front of them surged forwards, and Sanjay saw an official-looking man helping people onto the ride. Sanjay watched a group of teenagers climb excitedly into the colourful carriages. They chatted and giggled as they strapped the safety belts on tightly. With a loud clang and a clatter, the carriages shot forward.
20   Sanjay felt butterflies in his stomach. Suddenly the ride seemed very high and very fast. He wasn't sure that it looked fun after all. Before Sanjay could say anything, Dad turned around and took his hand.

"Come on, it's our turn!" he said.

The crowd hurried forward and Sanjay was swept through the gate. Dad led
25   him towards a carriage with a huge grin on his face.

"This is going to be fun!"

Answer these questions about the text that you've just read.
Circle the letter that matches the correct answer.

1.   What did Sanjay see when he first entered the theme park?

A   Lots of people
B   The gift shop
C   Some smaller rides
D   The Dinosaur Dipper
E   The café

2.   Why did Sanjay not go on the Dinosaur Dipper straight away?

A   He was frightened.
B   He didn't think it looked fun.
C   Maya wanted to go on it later.
D   The queue was too long.
E   They took Maya on some other rides first.

3.   Who did Sanjay see while he was waiting in the queue for the roller coaster?

A   A man selling ice creams
B   One of his friends from school
C   A man checking tickets
D   People taking photographs
E   Someone helping people onto the ride

4.   Which of the following statements is not true?

A   Sanjay and his dad queued for the ride for a long time.
B   The teenagers ahead of Sanjay put on their safety belts.
C   The teenagers ahead of Sanjay were nervous about the ride.
D   The ride made a loud sound as it set off.
E   The carriages moved very quickly when the ride set off.

5.   Which of these two words describe the Dinosaur Dipper?

A   Bright and colourful
B   Boring and empty
C   Tall and slow
D   Small and loopy
E   Fast and straight

/ 5

Carry on to the next question → →

Assessment Test 1

Answer these questions about the text that you've just read.
Circle the letter that matches the correct answer.

6. What does Sanjay think about the roller coaster when he reaches the end of the queue?

A He thinks it might break down.
B He thinks it will be really boring.
C He thinks it won't be very enjoyable.
D He thinks it will be exciting.
E He thinks it looks like a ride for small children.

7. Where is Maya while Sanjay and his dad are waiting to get on the Dinosaur Dipper?

A On a smaller ride
B With Mum in the café
C On the roller coaster already
D In the queue with them
E In the ticket office with Mum

/ 2

Answer these questions about the way words and phrases are used in the passage.

8. Which of these words is closest in meaning to "tugged" (line 2)?

A Touched
B Pulled
C Pushed
D Moaned
E Helped

9. Which of these words is closest in meaning to "chatted" (line 17)?

A Smiled
B Whispered
C Shouted
D Talked
E Laughed

10. What is meant by the expression "Sanjay was swept through the gate" (line 24)?

A Sanjay was pushed through the gate quickly.
B Sanjay fell over before he reached the gate.
C Sanjay walked calmly through the gate.
D Sanjay turned around and left the queue.
E Sanjay jumped over the gate.

/ 3

Answer these questions about the way words and phrases are used in the passage.

11. What type of words are "echoed" (line 8) and "begged" (line 9)?

A Nouns
B Adverbs
C Adjectives
D Verbs
E Similes

12. "Dad led him towards a carriage with a huge grin on his face" (lines 24-25).
Which of these words is an adjective?

A Dad
B towards
C carriage
D huge
E grin

/ 2

Choose the right word or phrase to fill the gap.
Circle the letter which matches the correct word.

13. Yesterday, Jen **ask say told speak telled** me all about the day she spent with
         A   B   C   D   E

14. Malik. She had asked me to go with them, but I **not couldn't do can would** go
         A   B   C   D   E

15. because I **are has will had is** to stay in to help my mum. Jen described the den
         A   B   C   D   E

16. they made in the woods. First, they tied a rope **until since between in though**
         A   B   C   D   E

17. two trees **and if while because soon** then put a plastic sheet over it. Next, they
         A   B   C   D   E

18. collected sticks and twigs **by if to so and** cover the sheet so it would blend
         A   B   C   D   E

19. into the trees. **Finally First Second But Once** , they put dried leaves on the
         A   B   C   D   E

20. floor of the den and **sat seated sitting seat sit** in it all afternoon.
         A   B   C   D   E

/ 8

Carry on to the next question → →

Assessment Test 1

In each sentence, there is one punctuation mistake. Circle the letter which matches the part of the sentence with the mistake.

21. Fran made a giant white chocolate and raspberry cake for her older brother's birthday?

    A   B   C   D   E

22. "Shut up! shouted Mum angrily, when the boys started to argue over the last ice lolly.

    A   B   C   D   E

23. I would'nt have believed that it was true if I hadn't seen it happen with my own eyes.

    A   B   C   D   E

24. While I was in London, I went to Buckingham Palace with, my friends Anne and John.

    A   B   C   D   E

25. The three naughty girl's quickly ran down the street, turned the corner and disappeared.

    A   B   C   D   E

/ 5

In each sentence, there is one spelling mistake. Circle the letter which matches the part of the sentence with the mistake.

26. The brave explorer slowly and carefully wallked across the rocky, narrow ledge to safety.

    A   B   C   D   E

27. George gave his sister a generous peace of chocolate cake and a big glass of lemonade.

    A   B   C   D   E

28. Edwin wasn't as good as Hasan at tennis, but he could eassely beat him at badminton.

    A   B   C   D   E

29. After a lot of thought, Julia decided to buy a skirt because the weather was so suny.

    A   B   C   D   E

30. The children all had a wonderfull time on their holiday in the south of Spain.

    A   B   C   D   E

/ 5

Total   / 30

End of Test

Assessment Test 2

Allow 30 minutes to do each test and work as quickly and as carefully as you can.

You can print **multiple-choice answer sheets** for these questions from our website — go to www.cgplearning.co.uk/11+. If you'd prefer to answer the questions on the page, just follow the instructions in the question.

> Read this passage carefully and answer the questions that follow.

Thank you letter

Dear Aunt Angela,

     I am writing to thank you for the present you gave me. I opened it on Christmas morning, but I must confess that I had peeled back a corner of the wrapping paper two days before. I had just got home from school and Mum was on the phone to Aunt
5 Glenda, so while her back was turned, I gave all my presents under the tree a squeeze. I could guess what most of them were, but I couldn't resist a quick peek at the one from you. When Mum saw that part of the paper had been ripped off she was furious and accused me of doing it, but I managed to convince her that Poppy had scratched it with her claws.

10   When I was finally allowed to open your present, I pretended to be surprised. I think I should have been given an award for my acting! I tore into the wrapping paper like a wild animal and gave a dramatic gasp when I opened it.

     I couldn't wait to play with your gift. I rushed into the garden, even though it was raining, and set up a goal post. I wanted to use Grandad's walking sticks, but they
15 wouldn't stand up by themselves, so I had to use one of Dad's garden gnomes and an upturned flowerpot instead. It was windy, so my first shot missed the goal by a mile and ended up near the shed, but my second shot hit the target fair and square! I ran around with my arms in the air to celebrate, just like the footballers on the television.

     Thanks again for the new football. It was definitely my favourite Christmas
20 present this year.

Love from,
Anita

Answer these questions about the text that you've just read.
Circle the letter that matches the correct answer.

1. What was the weather like when Anita went into the garden?

A It was windy and snowing.
B The air was still and it was sunny.
C The wind was blowing and it was raining.
D It was raining and cold.
E It was cold and sunny.

2. Why did Anita pretend to be surprised when she opened Aunt Angela's present?

A Anita didn't like the present.
B Someone had told Anita what was inside.
C Poppy had already ripped off the wrapping paper.
D Aunt Angela bought Anita the same gift every year.
E Anita had already seen part of the present.

3. Which of these words best describes the way that Anita opened Aunt Angela's present?

A Quickly
B Carefully
C Slowly
D Nervously
E Curiously

4. When did Anita try to guess what the presents were?

A Before school
B After dinner
C Late at night
D After school
E Before her bath

5. Who do you think Poppy is?

A Anita's big sister
B Anita's aunt
C Anita's next-door neighbour
D Anita's pet
E Anita's little sister

/ 5

Answer these questions about the text that you've just read.
Circle the letter that matches the correct answer.

6. What did Anita use as a goal?

A Poppy and a gnome
B A flowerpot and a gnome
C The shed
D The fence
E Grandad's walking sticks

7. Where did Anita's first shot go?

A On the shed roof
B Into the Christmas tree
C Near the shed
D In the next-door neighbour's garden
E In the goal

/ 2

Answer these questions about the way words and phrases are used in the passage.

8. Which of these words is closest in meaning to "ripped" (line 7)?

A Mended
B Smashed
C Torn
D Hurt
E Stolen

9. Which of these words is closest in meaning to "furious" (line 7)?

A Distracted
B Sad
C Disappointed
D Pleased
E Angry

10. Which of these words is closest in meaning to "surprised" (line 10)?

A Bored
B Annoyed
C Pleased
D Shocked
E Upset

/ 3

Carry on to the next question → →

> Answer these questions about the way words and phrases are used in the passage.

11. "I tore into the wrapping paper like a wild animal" (lines 11-12).
    What technique is this an example of?

    A A metaphor
    B A simile
    C A synonym
    D Alliteration
    E A homophone

12. "my first shot missed the goal by a mile" (line 16).
    Which of these words is a verb?

    A first
    B shot
    C missed
    D by
    E mile

/ 2

> In each sentence, there is one spelling mistake. Circle the
> letter which matches the part of the sentence with the mistake.

13. Nobody herd the thief as he sneaked through the open window of the empty house.

    A   B   C   D   E

14. I could not sleep last night because the babys were crying and wailing until midnight.

    A   B   C   D   E

15. Nirav's sister was allmost tall enough to reach the top shelf of the kitchen cupboard.

    A   B   C   D   E

16. Joby was really looking forward to the tastey Sunday lunch at his grandma's house.

    A   B   C   D   E

17. "You certainly won't be able to get there if you don't now the way," warned Donna.

    A   B   C   D   E

18. The teacher explained how to use the sissors so the children wouldn't cut themselves.

    A   B   C   D   E

19. The Dion family had to move house last year because of the terrable floods.

    A   B   C   D   E

20. Tariq wrote the adress for Mary's flat with a pencil on a piece of scrap paper.

    A   B   C   D   E

/ 8

> Choose the right word or phrase to fill the gap.
> Circle the letter which matches the correct word.

21. We watched the startled family of **deer** **deers** **deeres** **deeries** **dear** run into the
    A   B   C   D   E

22. forest. As we walked away, **us** **our** **my** **I** **me** noticed that one of the animals
    A B C D E

23. was still nearby. It was **drink** **thirsty** **drank** **drinking** **dranked** from a puddle
    A   B   C   D   E

24. and hadn't **look** **saw** **looked** **sees** **seen** us. When it looked up, it froze for a
    A B C D E

25. second before running **after** **away** **quickly** **slowly** **off** its family.
    A   B   C   D   E

/ 5

> In each sentence, there is one punctuation mistake. Circle the
> letter which matches the part of the sentence with the mistake.

26. "What is the point of using punctuation properly!" asked Robert with a huge grin.
    A   B   C   D   E

27. The chocolate cake had risen perfectly and Rita thought that it looked ready to be iced
    A   B   C   D   E

28. If I'd known, how tired you were going to be after work, I'd have cooked dinner myself.
    A   B   C   D   E

29. Yvonnes washing was all over the garden and in the street because of the strong wind.
    A   B   C   D   E

30. Naava visited a wonderful old Castle during the school's annual summer trip to Wales.
    A   B   C   D   E

/ 5

Total | / 30

End of Test

Assessment Test 2

Assessment Test 3

Allow 30 minutes to do each test and work as quickly and as carefully as you can.

You can print **multiple-choice answer sheets** for these questions from our website — go to www.cgplearning.co.uk/11+. If you'd prefer to answer the questions on the page, just follow the instructions in the question.

> Read this passage carefully and answer the questions that follow.

Roger's Records

"Dad?"

"What now?" Roger's father said wearily, without looking up from his newspaper.

"Guess how old Robert Wadlow was when he could carry his father up the stairs."

"I've no idea," said Roger's father.

5   "Have a guess," Roger insisted.

"Twelve."

"Wrong! It says here that Robert Pershing Wadlow, the tallest man that ever lived, was nine years old. That's the same age as me!"

Mr Cherry had been forced to listen to many of these fascinating facts from

10 his son, but he had only himself to blame. It was his idea to buy Roger his first 'Book of World Records' three years ago and he had given his son the new edition every Christmas since then.

"Dad?"

"Yes, son."

15   "What do you think the record is for the furthest distance for spitting a watermelon seed?"

"Ten metres," said Mr Cherry, reading the same sentence in his newspaper for the fifth time.

"Wrong! It's actually seventy three metres!" yelled Roger triumphantly.

20   He loved it when his father got the answer wrong. He was a teacher but he didn't know his records. Roger searched for another killer question. He knew that he probably only had time for one more before his father's patience ran out. He started reading about the woman with the longest fingernails in the world.

"Dad?"

25   There was no reply. Roger looked across the living room at an outspread newspaper that seemed to have sprouted legs and feet. The feet were wearing tartan slippers, and coming from behind the newspaper was a sound like the breathing of a wounded warthog. Roger wondered if there was a record for the loudest snoring in the world!

Answer these questions about the text that you've just read.
Circle the letter that matches the correct answer.

1. How old is Roger?

A Six
B Seven
C Eight
D Nine
E Ten

2. According to the text, what could Robert Pershing Wadlow do?

A Carry his father up the stairs
B Spit watermelon seeds
C Grow really long finger nails
D Tell his father annoying facts
E Snore louder than anyone else in the world

3. When does Roger receive each year's 'Book of World Records'?

A On his birthday
B At Christmas
C Every January
D At Easter
E When he has been good

4. What is Roger's father's job?

A Journalist
B Teacher
C Writer for the 'Book of World Records'
D Policeman
E Builder

5. Which word best describes how Roger's father feels about Roger's questions?

A Confused
B Proud
C Furious
D Happy
E Uninterested

/ 5

Carry on to the next question → →

Assessment Test 3

Answer these questions about the text that you've just read.
Circle the letter that matches the correct answer.

6. Which of these records is not mentioned in the story?

A The World's furthest seed spit
B The World's tallest man
C The World's longest fingernails
D The World's best-selling book
E The World's loudest snore

7. Why does Roger's father not reply to Roger's final question?

A He has already left the room.
B He refuses to answer any more questions.
C He has fallen asleep.
D He is concentrating on reading.
E He is watching a cartoon on television.

/ 2

Answer these questions about the way words and phrases are used in the passage.

8. Which of these words is closest in meaning to "yelled" (line 19)?

A Shouted
B Laughed
C Said
D Whispered
E Begged

9. Which of these words is closest in meaning to "fascinating" (line 9)?

A Wrong
B Boring
C Out-of-date
D Interesting
E Correct

10. Which of these words is closest in meaning to "sprouted" (line 26)?

A Appeared
B Walked
C Lost
D Grown
E Eaten

/ 3

Answer these questions about the way words and phrases are used in the passage.

11. "a sound like the breathing of a wounded warthog." (lines 27-28)
Which of the following words is an adjective?

A sound
B like
C breathing
D wounded
E warthog

12. "Roger" (line 5) and "Christmas" (line 12) are examples of which part of speech?

A Common nouns
B Verbs
C Adjectives
D Proper nouns
E Pronouns

/ 2

In each sentence, there is one punctuation mistake. Circle the letter which matches the part of the sentence with the mistake.

13. The boys' mother took Them both to the cinema to see a film called 'Star Battle Heroes'.
    A   B   C   D   E

14. "I'm sure that you'll really enjoy yourself if you come with us to play in the park?"
    A   B   C   D   E

15. The ingredients I need to make the cake are flour, butter, sugar eggs and skimmed milk.
    A   B   C   D   E

16. "I'm going to leave on Wednesday morning," he said, although nobody believed him".
    A   B   C   D   E

17. Hannah and her family lived in a small house in the village of oakthorpe.
    A   B   C   D   E

18. Raj's grandfather cant' wait to retire because it means that he'll get a free bus pass.
    A   B   C   D   E

19. Great Britain's population is more than 60 million and it continues to, grow every day.
    A   B   C   D   E

20. "Have you ever been on holiday to France, Italy, Austria or Spain? asked John.
    A   B   C   D   E

/ 8

Carry on to the next question → →

Assessment Test 3

In each sentence, there is one spelling mistake. Circle the letter which matches the part of the sentence with the mistake.

21. The teacher did not believe Feng's exscuse for not doing her weekly science homework.
    A   B   C   D   E

22. They were forty kilometres from their destinasion when the train came to a sudden halt.
    A   B   C   D   E

23. While most of the children ran accross the yard, Rosie preferred to hop on one leg.
    A   B   C   D   E

24. I wish that Nathaniel would stop asking questions because it's nun of his business!
    A   B   C   D   E

25. When the alarm rang, the children kept carm and left the building quickly and quietly.
    A   B   C   D   E

(/ 5)

Choose the right word or phrase to fill the gap.
Circle the letter which matches the correct word.

26. When we went to the zoo on Friday, I saw **a an some two none** elephant. It was
                                              A B   C   D   E

27. bigger than I **has had is will am** imagined. As we watched, it started
                   A   B   C   D   E

28. playing in a large pond **by up between down far** the fence. After a few
                             A   B   C   D   E

29. minutes, the elephant **begin beginned start begunned began** to spray
                           A   B   C   D   E

30. water over the crowd! The zookeeper could **be no of not to** stop laughing.
                                               A   B   C   D   E

(/ 5)

(Total   / 30)

End of Test

Assessment Test 3

Assessment Test 4

Allow 30 minutes to do each test and work as quickly and as carefully as you can.

You can print **multiple-choice answer sheets** for these questions from our website — go to www.cgplearning.co.uk/11+. If you'd prefer to answer the questions on the page, just follow the instructions in the question.

> Read this passage carefully and answer the questions that follow.

Castles

After the Normans invaded England in 1066, they immediately started to build castles all around the country. These castles were not just ordinary buildings, but were fortresses to protect Norman soldiers from their enemies.

The earliest Norman castles were either made within an existing Roman
5   fort or were 'motte and bailey' castles. The word 'motte' means a natural or man-made mound and the word 'bailey' means an enclosure. The bailey was a yard area which was surrounded by a wall. These castles were built by local peasants and could be constructed quickly. Once they had dug a deep, circular ditch, they piled the earth from the ditch into the centre to form the high hill
10 known as the motte. A wooden building called a 'keep' was built on top of the motte as a look-out point. The keep was at the top of the motte, so it would have been difficult for enemy troops to attack it. The deep ditch around the castle also helped to protect it from invaders.

A courtyard was built next to the motte, and this was known as the bailey.
15 There were many buildings within the bailey, including stables, storerooms, kitchens and living quarters. Many of the castle's workers lived and worked inside the bailey. The bailey was often surrounded by a palisade. This was a tall fence made using wooden stakes and was an important part of the castle's defence.

Motte and bailey castles were quick and cheap to build and provided good
20 defence against the enemy. However, they were built out of wood, so they caught fire easily. Over time, people started building castles out of stone because they lasted longer and to prevent them from burning down.

> Answer these questions about the text that you've just read.
> Circle the letter that matches the correct answer.

1. According to the text, what is a 'bailey'?

A A hill
B A courtyard
C A fortress
D A Roman soldier
E A castle

2. Which of the following was an important part of the castle's defence?

A The bailey
B The kitchens
C The palisade
D Local peasants
E The wooden buildings

3. Which of the following is not given as a reason why the Normans built motte and bailey castles?

A They were very big.
B They were quick to build.
C They were difficult to attack.
D They were cheap to build.
E They provided good defence.

4. According to the text, which of the following buildings was not in the bailey?

A The kitchens
B The stables
C Living quarters
D Storerooms
E The school

5. Which of the following does not describe a 'motte'?

A A natural mound
B A heap of earth
C A high hill
D A Roman fort
E Part of a castle

/ 5

Answer these questions about the text that you've just read.
Circle the letter that matches the correct answer.

6. According to the text, what was the purpose of the castle's 'keep'?

A To attack from
B To keep animals in
C To store weapons in
D To watch for enemies
E To walk around

7. According to the passage, why were later castles built out of stone instead of wood?

A Stone was cheaper.
B Wood was running out.
C There was more stone available.
D Wood could catch fire.
E Stone was difficult to attack.

/ 2

Answer these questions about the way words and phrases are used in the passage.

8. Which of these words is closest in meaning to "prevent" (line 22)?

A Help
B Watch
C Rescue
D Stop
E Go

9. Which of these words is closest in meaning to "invaders" (line 13)?

A Armies
B Attackers
C Friends
D Defenders
E Builders

10. Which of these words is closest in meaning to "circular" (line 8)?

A Long
B Round
C Around
D Wide
E Smooth

/ 3

Carry on to the next question → →

11. "they were built out of wood, so they caught fire easily" (line 20-21).
    Which of these words is an adverb?

A they
B built
C wood
D fire
E easily

12. "deep" (line 8) and "cheap" (line 19) are examples of which part of speech?

A Adjectives
B Adverbs
C Nouns
D Verbs
E Pronouns

/ 2

13. Elliot always rushs his homework so that he can go and play rugby with his friends.
    A   B   C   D   E

14. Matilda couldn't believe that Bruce had eaten the hole chocolate cake in one go.
    A   B   C   D   E

15. Their was enough time to make sure that all the children had a turn on the trampoline.
    A   B   C   D   E

16. The female community choir won seccond place in the national talent show.
    A   B   C   D   E

17. Sumana ran straight threw the hall and out into the playground without stopping.
    A   B   C   D   E

18. The whether was fine so the family decided to have a picnic in the park at lunchtime.
    A   B   C   D   E

19. Mario was feeling very energetick, so he went for a long run before he played hockey.
    A   B   C   D   E

20. Nafisa had been expecting a bycycle so the present wasn't much of a surprise.
    A   B   C   D   E

/ 8

In each sentence, there is one punctuation mistake. Circle the letter which matches the part of the sentence with the mistake.

21. "do you think Kevin will arrive in time for the last train to Beverley?" asked Anne.
    A — B — C — D — E

22. Billy, Salim, john, Kyle, Harry and Tim all turned up late for their science class.
    A — B — C — D — E

23. Even though theres heavy snow, they still want to play football in the park.
    A — B — C — D — E

24. "Have you seen my new blue coat" asked Ewa, looking around the room sadly.
    A — B — C — D — E

25. Georgina took a deep breath and then yelled, Ready or not, here I come!"
    A — B — C — D — E

/ 5

Choose the right word or phrase to fill the gap.
Circle the letter which matches the correct word.

26. "Can I have **a one some few an** grapes, please?" asked Mrs Rhency. Mr Apple,
             A B C   D E

27. the greengrocer, took a bunch from a shelf **behind across between through to**
                                               A   B   C   D E

28. him. He smiled at Mrs Rhency, who **are were will be has was** his favourite
                                          A   B   C   D E

29. customer. She **byes bought buy brings bys** all her fruit and vegetables from
                       A   B   C   D   E

30. him **even too with and if** she usually had a piece of local gossip to tell him.
        A B C D E

/ 5

Total / 30

End of Test

Assessment Test 4

Assessment Test 5

Allow 30 minutes to do each test and work as quickly and as carefully as you can.

You can print **multiple-choice answer sheets** for these questions from our website — go to www.cgplearning.co.uk/11+. If you'd prefer to answer the questions on the page, just follow the instructions in the question.

> Read this poem carefully and answer the questions that follow.

The Fieldmouse

Where the acorn tumbles down,
Where the ash tree sheds its berry,
With your fur so soft and brown,
With your eye so round and merry,
5   Scarcely moving the long grass,
Fieldmouse, I can see you pass.

Little thing, in what dark den,
Lie you all the winter sleeping?
Till warm weather comes again,
10   Then once more I see you peeping
Round about the tall tree roots,
Nibbling at their fallen fruits.

Fieldmouse, fieldmouse, do not go,
Where the farmer stacks his treasure,
15   Find the nut that falls below,
Eat the acorn at your pleasure,
But you must not steal the grain
He has stacked with so much pain.

Make your hole where mosses spring,
20   Underneath the tall oak's shadow,
Pretty, quiet harmless thing,
Play about the sunny meadow.
Keep away from corn and house,
None will harm you, little mouse.

by Cecil Frances Alexander

Answer these questions about the text that you've just read.
Circle the letter that matches the correct answer.

1. What does the fieldmouse do in the winter?

A It sleeps in a dark den.
B It moves somewhere warmer.
C It stores nuts and fruit.
D It plays in the meadow.
E It eats lots of food.

2. According to the poem, what should the fieldmouse not eat?

A Acorns
B Fruits
C Tree roots
D Berries
E Corn

3. Which of these words best describes the fieldmouse?

A Fat and happy
B Sad and anxious
C Pretty and gentle
D Harmful and noisy
E Hungry and tired

4. Which of these statements about the farmer is true?

A He is very rich.
B He stores grain.
C He is ill.
D He is sleepy.
E He is merry.

5. Where does the poet tell the fieldmouse to make its den in verse 4?

A In the long grass
B Under the ash tree
C Under the oak tree
D In the meadow
E Inside the house

/ 5

Carry on to the next question → →

52

6. Which of these does the fieldmouse not do?

A Find food
B Eat
C Play
D Go to the farmer's house
E Make a nest

7. Why does the fieldmouse "scarcely" (line 5) move the grass?

A Because the fieldmouse is so small
B Because the fieldmouse's fur is so soft
C Because the grass is so heavy
D Because the fieldmouse is so fast
E Because the fieldmouse is sleeping

/ 2

Answer these questions about the way words and phrases are used in the poem.

8. Which of these words is closest in meaning to "nibbling" (line 12)?

A Chewing
B Chattering
C Gulping
D Looking
E Destroying

9. Which of these words is closest in meaning to "stacks" (line 14)?

A Produces
B Scatters
C Sells
D Counts
E Heaps

10. Which of these words is closest in meaning to "sheds" (line 2)?

A Huts
B Grows
C Drops
D Finds
E Shows

/ 3

Answer these questions about the way words and phrases are used in the poem.

11. What types of words are "soft" (line 3) and "merry" (line 4)?

A Verbs
B Nouns
C Adverbs
D Adjectives
E Pronouns

12. "Find the nut that falls below" (line 15).
Which of these words is a verb?

A Find
B the
C nut
D that
E below

/ 2

Choose the right word or phrase to fill the gap.
Circle the letter which matches the correct word.

13. Today we are **going go to goes went** shopping for decorations for my party.
     A B C D E

14. Hopefully we'll be able to buy some pirate flags **or why because therefore then**
 A B C D E

15. I'm having a pirate party. Everyone is going to **were ware where wear wears**
 A B C D E

16. fancy dress. I've got an eyepatch and a sword, and I **are is am have been** going
 A B C D E

17. to paint a beard on my face **for too two as to** . Mum has booked a bouncy castle,
 A B C D E

18. and Dad is baking a birthday cake. I haven't decided **what when how who that**
 A B C D E

19. I'm going to invite yet, **and or but if when** my best friends Loreen, Ravi and
 A B C D E

20. Peter have **saying says speak say said** that they've already bought their outfits.
 A B C D E

/ 8

Carry on to the next question → →

Assessment Test 5

In each sentence, there is one punctuation mistake. Circle the letter which matches the part of the sentence with the mistake.

21. Wild animals like hedgehogs owls and deer can all be found at the rescue centre.

     A   B   C   D   E

22. "How many lengths of the pool did you swim" Liam asked his older brother.

     A   B   C   D   E

23. "Please put the tablecloth on the table ready for the cake sale, Joya said politely.

     A   B   C   D   E

24. My teacher, mr Gerard, has organised a concert and a play at the community centre.

     A   B   C   D   E

25. If its raining over the weekend, Mum says she'll take us bowling and to the cinema.

     A   B   C   D   E

/ 5

In each sentence, there is one spelling mistake. Circle the letter which matches the part of the sentence with the mistake.

26. When Abdullah woke up, he polished his new bicycle untill it glistened in the sun.

     A   B   C   D   E

27. Jenny liked to push her tongue against her tooth and make it woble like a rocking horse.

     A   B   C   D   E

28. The signed football was Fatima's favourite possession and she didn't want to loose it.

     A   B   C   D   E

29. The puppys were adorable, but Sam knew he would not be allowed to keep one.

     A   B   C   D   E

30. Harry liked hiding in the cupboard under the stares when he played hide and seek.

     A   B   C   D   E

/ 5

Total   / 30

End of Test

Assessment Test 6

Allow 30 minutes to do each test and work as quickly and as carefully as you can.

You can print **multiple-choice answer sheets** for these questions from our website — go to www.cgplearning.co.uk/11+. If you'd prefer to answer the questions on the page, just follow the instructions in the question.

> Read this passage carefully and answer the questions that follow.

Aunt Florence

Some people thought that Ruby's aunt was slightly odd. Aunt Florence wore multi-coloured clothes, dyed her long hair as red as a post box and had peculiar habits (singing in the supermarket was a particularly embarrassing one). Ruby's older brother Alfie said that she got confused about what was real and what was imaginary.
5 Alfie said that this was because Aunt Florence was a writer, but Ruby believed everything she said.

The day before yesterday, Aunt Flo had given Ruby a key: a thick, rusty, unimpressive-looking key. It looked as if it had not turned a lock in a long, long time, Ruby thought. Lowering her voice, Aunt Flo had told Ruby that it opened a
10 secret door in the attic of Grandpa's house; a door which led to another world. This was an enchanted world of magical people and strange creatures; a world Flo herself had visited when she was Ruby's age.

"The door will only reveal itself," Ruby's aunt had whispered, "if the person holding the key believes that the magical door exists."
15 Now Ruby was standing alone in the dusty, disorderly, dimly-lit attic, holding the key. Grandpa's old train set was laid out in the middle of the floor, as if he had just been playing with it. Around the train set were boxes and books and old photo albums, all piled high. But there was no sign of a door.

"Where are you? I know you are here, somewhere," Ruby said quietly as she
20 searched the room.

Suddenly, the walls began to shake. Mortar crumbled from between the bricks and spiders scurried away from their cobwebs. Ruby stared in astonishment as a wonky, wooden door slowly appeared in the wall.

Answer these questions about the text that you've just read.
Circle the letter that matches the correct answer.

1. Which statement about Aunt Florence is not true?

A   She has a niece and a nephew.
B   She wears colourful clothes.
C   She has strange habits.
D   She has short hair.
E   She sings in public.

2. When did Aunt Florence give Ruby the key?

A   Two days ago
B   One week ago
C   One day ago
D   Two weeks ago
E   Three days ago

3. How did Aunt Florence speak to Ruby when she gave her the key?

A   Quickly
B   Loudly
C   Quietly
D   Angrily
E   Jokingly

4. How did Aunt Florence know about the door?

A   She had gone through it a few days ago.
B   Grandpa had told her about it last year.
C   Her older brother had told her about it.
D   She had written about it in one of her books.
E   She had gone through it when she was younger.

5. Which of the following statements about the attic is not true?

A   It was untidy.
B   It was dark.
C   It was dirty.
D   It was in Aunt Florence's house.
E   It was filled with boxes and other old things.

/ 5

Answer these questions about the text that you've just read.
Circle the letter that matches the correct answer.

6. What does Ruby have to do to reveal the door to the enchanted world?

A Tell the door to reveal itself.
B Turn the key clockwise in the keyhole.
C Believe that the door exists.
D Rub the key until it shines.
E Tap the wall three times.

7. Why did Ruby look at the door "in astonishment" (line 22)?

A The door was made of gold.
B The door was covered in cobwebs.
C The door was breaking apart.
D The door was open.
E The door had appeared from nowhere.

/ 2

Answer these questions about the way words and phrases are used in the passage.

8. The word "imaginary" (line 4) could most accurately be replaced by:

A factual.
B dishonest.
C honest.
D invented.
E copied.

9. Which of these words is closest in meaning to "reveal" (line 13)?

A Find
B Unlock
C Show
D Open
E Hide

10. Which of these words is closest in meaning to the word "unimpressive" (line 8)?

A Ordinary
B Unusual
C Unclear
D Rare
E Amazing

/ 3

Carry on to the next question →→

Answer these questions about the way words and phrases are used in the passage.

11. "Ruby said quietly as she searched the room" (lines 19-20).
Which of these words is an adverb?

A Ruby
B said
C quietly
D searched
E room

12. "dusty, disorderly, dimly-lit" (line 15). This is an example of:

A a rhyme.
B alliteration.
C a simile.
D a metaphor.
E onomatopoeia.

/ 2

In each sentence, there is one punctuation mistake. Circle the letter which matches the part of the sentence with the mistake.

13. There are free reading group's for children in the library every Saturday morning.
    A   B   C   D   E

14. Great-Grandma and her friends went on a coach trip to Milton Keynes for her Birthday.
    A   B   C   D   E

15. Remote-controlled battling robots are going to be one of the top-selling toys this year?
    A   B   C   D   E

16. Holidays are a time to relax, play, try new activities, and spend time with family.
    A   B   C   D   E

17. Is the new sports centre going to open to the public in the summer or autumn!
    A   B   C   D   E

18. It was Lord Freds job to defend his castle, battle evil armies and to fight for the king.
    A   B   C   D   E

19. "Help me, please help! screeched the baker, as a cheeky mouse scurried across the floor.
    A   B   C   D   E

20. Its really important for your health to eat some fruit and vegetables every day.
    A   B   C   D   E

/ 8

In each sentence, there is one spelling mistake. Circle the letter which matches the part of the sentence with the mistake.

21. Amber handed out loads of copys of her flyer on how to recycle household rubbish.
    A   B   C   D   E

22. As a spesial favour to his dad, Matthew took his sister to the optician on Monday.
    A   B   C   D   E

23. Holly peared through the gaps between the shrubs and trees, looking for her dog.
    A   B   C   D   E

24. Ibrahim worked hard in his gitar lessons so that he would be ready for the concert.
    A   B   C   D   E

25. Laila needed help because the knot in the skipping rope was tide so tightly.
    A   B   C   D   E

/ 5

Choose the right word or phrase to fill the gap. Circle the letter which matches the correct word.

26. Yesterday I had to go to the dentist and I **aren't hadn't weren't isn't wasn't**
                     A   B   C   D   E

27. looking forward to it. However, **if when but how on** I got there, the dentist
            A   B   C   D   E

28. **looks seen looked look saw** at my teeth and said that they were the best teeth
    A   B   C   D   E

29. she **had have hadn't has hasn't** seen all week. Then she gave me a sticker
        A   B   C   D   E

30. and **said tells tell told says** me to keep up the good work.
        A   B   C   D   E

/ 5

Total   / 30

End of Test

Assessment Test 6

Assessment Test 7

Allow 30 minutes to do each test and work as quickly and as carefully as you can.

You can print **multiple-choice answer sheets** for these questions from our website — go to www.cgplearning.co.uk/11+. If you'd prefer to answer the questions on the page, just follow the instructions in the question.

> Read this passage carefully and answer the questions that follow.

The Ancient Olympics

The first Olympic Games were held nearly 3000 years ago in Greece. They were held to honour Zeus, king of the gods, and took place in a stadium in the valley of Olympia. The Olympics were celebrated every four years as a sporting and religious festival and could draw large crowds of up to 40,000 people.

5   The games started with worship in a great temple near the stadium. A specially-carved statue of Zeus made from gold and ivory, six times bigger than the average man, was the focus of the celebrations. The competitors had to swear an oath* to Zeus that they had trained for ten months to prepare for the events.

After the ceremony, the games began. One of the most demanding events was
10   the pentathlon. This consisted of five activities: running, throwing the javelin (a spear), throwing a discus (a metal disc), wrestling and long jump, and required great strength and determination from the athletes. The final race of the games was the challenging hoplite race, where the runners had to wear armour and carry shields. The winner of each Olympic event was presented with a special crown made from
15   olive leaves.

The Olympic Games were held for over a thousand years until they were banned by the Romans. They were restarted as the modern Olympics in 1896. The modern games include many of the same events as the ancient games, such as races and the long jump, as well as new activities like swimming and fencing. Although the
20   Olympics are now held all over the world, they are still celebrated every four years.

*oath — *promise*

Answer these questions about the text that you've just read.
Circle the letter that matches the correct answer.

1. Where did the sporting events of the Ancient Olympics take place?

A   In the great temple
B   In a stadium in Olympia
C   In a different district every four years
D   In stadiums all over the world
E   In the mountains of Greece

2. For how long were the Ancient Olympics held before being banned?

A   40,000 years
B   more than 3000 years
C   more than 1000 years
D   1896 years
E   less than 4 years

3. What did the winners receive?

A   Gold and ivory
B   A specially-carved statue of Zeus
C   A medal
D   A chariot
E   A crown made of leaves

4. According to the text, which of the following statements about Zeus is not true?

A   Zeus was king of the gods.
B   The games ended with everybody worshipping Zeus.
C   The statue of Zeus was taller than a man.
D   All the athletes made a promise to Zeus.
E   The Olympic Games were held to honour Zeus.

5. Why was the hoplite race difficult?

A   It was the final race of the games.
B   It was the last event in the pentathlon.
C   The runners had travelled from all over Greece.
D   The runners had to run long distances.
E   The runners had to wear heavy armour.

/ 5

Carry on to the next question → →

62

> Answer these questions about the text that you've just read.
> Circle the letter that matches the correct answer.

6. Which of the following does not describe the Ancient Olympic Games?

A It was a sporting festival.
B It was held to honour Zeus.
C It could draw large crowds of thousands of people.
D It was dedicated to the king of the Greeks.
E It was a religious festival.

7. Which of the following words describes the statue of Zeus?

A Ugly
B Shabby
C Impressive
D Ignored
E Small

/ 2

> Answer these questions about the way words and phrases are used in the passage.

8. Which of these phrases means the same as "to honour Zeus" (line 2)?

A To crown Zeus
B To ask Zeus for a favour
C To visit Zeus
D To vote for Zeus
E To praise Zeus

9. Which of these words is closest in meaning to "competitors" (line 7)?

A Contestants
B Men
C Priests
D People
E Audience

10. Which of these words could most accurately replace "strength" (line 12)?

A Power
B Muscles
C Training
D Skill
E Size

/ 3

Answer these questions about the way words and phrases are used in the passage.

11. "great" (line 5) and "special" (line 14) are examples of which part of speech?

A   Nouns
B   Verbs
C   Adverbs
D   Adjectives
E   Pronouns

12. "The modern games include many of the same events" (line 17-18).
Which of these words is a verb?

A   modern
B   games
C   include
D   many
E   same

/ 2

In each sentence, there is one spelling mistake. Circle the
letter which matches the part of the sentence with the mistake.

13. Dangerus materials, such as fireworks, must be kept away from children for their safety.
     A   B   C   D   E

14. The audition was really tuff, but Georgina knew she had done her best when it was over.
     A   B   C   D   E

15. The hairy monkies at the zoo were wonderful and sent Dad rushing for his camera.
     A   B   C   D   E

16. Jokeingly, Grandpa placed a rubber spider and a rotten egg in Mum's wellington boot.
     A   B   C   D   E

17. The pirates swore they never toucht the captain's chocolate, but the parrot disagreed.
     A   B   C   D   E

18. The princess hated being throne over people's shoulders when they rescued her.
     A   B   C   D   E

19. The vampire had a memerable visit to the dentist's and said he'd never visit him again.
     A   B   C   D   E

20. The waiter brought knifes, forks, spoons and glasses to the table, but forgot the food.
     A   B   C   D   E

/ 8

Carry on to the next question → →

> Choose the right word or phrase to fill the gap.
> Circle the letter which matches the correct word.

21. The netball team are celebrating **some an lots many one** great news.
   A   B   C   D   E

22. They have **lifted went beaten left won** the finals of the national championships!
    A   B   C   D   E

23. At first, they **made make may makes maid** us all believe that they
     A   B   C   D   E

24. **have did has had would** lost. We knew they were tricking us though, because
    A   B   C   D   E

25. they couldn't stop smiling! There **is will was were have** be a party to celebrate.
                                    A   B   C   D   E

/ 5

> In each sentence, there is one punctuation mistake. Circle the
> letter which matches the part of the sentence with the mistake.

26. The umpire said that the batsman was out, even though he hadnt touched the ball.
        A   B   C   D   E

27. As she polished the car, Razia hoped that her dad would let her go to the park".
        A   B   C   D   E

28. Although he was only six, Ben loved reading books' about racing motorbikes.
        A   B   C   D   E

29. Alex found that planting Trees for the new woodland by the river was fun and rewarding.
        A   B   C   D   E

30. Amir went on the carousel, the spinning teacups the dodgems and the big wheel.
        A   B   C   D   E

/ 5

Total   / 30

End of Test

Assessment Test 8

Allow 30 minutes to do each test and work as quickly and as carefully as you can.

You can print **multiple-choice answer sheets** for these questions from our website — go to www.cgplearning.co.uk/11+. If you'd prefer to answer the questions on the page, just follow the instructions in the question.

> Read this poem carefully and answer the questions that follow.

Winter Time

Late lies the wintry sun a-bed,
A frosty, fiery sleepy-head;
Blinks but an hour or two; and then,
A blood-red orange, sets again.

5 Before the stars have left the skies,
At morning in the dark I rise;
And shivering in my nakedness,
By the cold candle, bathe and dress.

Close by the jolly fire I sit
10 To warm my frozen bones a bit;
Or with a reindeer-sled, explore
The colder countries round the door.

When to go out, my nurse doth wrap
Me in my comforter* and cap;
15 The cold wind burns my face, and blows
Its frosty pepper up my nose.

Black are my steps on silver sod**;
Thick blows my frosty breath abroad;
And tree and house, and hill and lake,
20 Are frosted like a wedding-cake.

by Robert Louis Stevenson

*comforter — *a scarf*
**sod — *soil*

Answer these questions about the text that you've just read.
Circle the letter that matches the correct answer.

1. Which of these things is not mentioned in the poem?

A Sun
B Fire
C Candle
D Stars
E Moon

2. What does the nurse do?

A Make clothes for the child.
B Put the child to bed.
C Dress the child.
D Wake the child up.
E Take the child out to play.

3. Why does the child dress by candlelight?

A The child is cold.
B It is night time.
C It is dark in the morning.
D The child doesn't want to wake anyone else.
E The child is scared of the dark.

4. What happens in lines 15-16?

A The wind has black specks in it.
B The wind is so hot that it burns the child's face.
C Somebody spills pepper.
D The wind is so cold that it stings the child's face.
E The child can't stop sneezing.

5. Which of these events happens last in the poem?

A The child goes outside.
B The child gets up in the dark.
C The child shivers in the candlelight.
D The child washes and gets dressed.
E The child gets warm by the fire.

/ 5

Answer these questions about the text that you've just read.
Circle the letter that matches the correct answer.

6. What is the first verse about?

A The stars twinkling in the sky.
B The sun melting the snow.
C The sun rising and setting.
D The child getting up late.
E The child playing in the sun.

7. In line 17, the child notices that the frost is melted by:

A the rain.
B pepper.
C the fire.
D the reindeer sled.
E footsteps.

/ 2

Answer these questions about the way words and phrases are used in the poem.

8. Which of these words is closest in meaning to "shivering" (line 7)?

A Trembling
B Sobbing
C Heating
D Hurting
E Freezing

9. Which of these words is closest in meaning to "jolly" (line 9)?

A Merry
B Friendly
C Warm
D Excited
E Funny

10. Which of the following is closest in meaning to "explore" (line 11)?

A Move from
B Travel around
C Arrive
D Depart from
E Admire

/ 3

Carry on to the next question → →

68

> Answer these questions about the way words and phrases are used in the poem.

11. "To warm my frozen bones a bit" (line 10). Which of these words is an adjective?

A warm
B my
C frozen
D bones
E bit

12. "hill and lake, / Are frosted like a wedding-cake." (lines 19-20). This is an example of:

A a metaphor.
B a simile.
C a question.
D an apostrophe.
E an exclamation.

/ 2

> In each sentence, there is one punctuation mistake. Circle the letter which matches the part of the sentence with the mistake.

13. Ross was hoping to invite Josh, Sven Peter and Andy to the evening football match.
   A   B   C   D   E

14. Brian's children, Ana and Sam, were really looking forward to their holiday in france.
   A   B   C   D   E

15. Mrs Jones was determined, to finish her novel and worked hard on it every day.
   A   B   C   D   E

16. The tiger which looked as though it was asleep, suddenly jumped up with a roar!
   A   B   C   D   E

17. After walking on the moor, Phil's shoes were covered in thick, mud, grass and leaves.
   A   B   C   D   E

18. The evil mouse threatened the terrified crowd, Give me all your cheese or else!"
   A   B   C   D   E

19. The ballet class are really excited because theyre going to London to see Swan Lake.
   A   B   C   D   E

20. Parvati hid behind a cushion and said, trembling, "This part of the film is really scary"!
   A   B   C   D   E

/ 8

Assessment Test 8

In each sentence, there is one spelling mistake. Circle the
letter which matches the part of the sentence with the mistake.

21. The pilot landed the plane safely on the runway during the awfull storm.

      A   B   C   D   E

22. The cat was a pityful sight when she came in looking like a drowned rat.

    A   B   C   D   E

23. Many people believe that you will get seven years bad luck if you brake a mirror.

    A   B   C   D   E

24. Ice skating is really fun and has become very populer on outdoor rinks at Christmas.

    A   B   C   D   E

25. The duckling waddled across the garden, draging a wiggling worm along behind it.

    A   B   C   D   E

/ 5

Choose the right word or phrase to fill the gap.
Circle the letter which matches the correct word.

26. Riding a unicycle requires an excellent sense **if about in to of** balance.

          A   B   C D E

27. I **bought bring brought buy buyed** one from a junk shop last week and

   A   B   C   D   E

28. I've been practising in the park **away beside next in front between** our house.

         A   B   C   D   E

29. At first, I **wouldn't haven't mustn't couldn't shouldn't** even stay upright

        A   B   C   D   E

30. for two seconds, but now I can **rode riding ride rider rid** with my eyes closed!

         A   B   C   D   E

/ 5

Total   / 30

End of Test

Assessment Test 8

Glossary

adjective	A word that <u>describes</u> a <u>noun</u>, e.g. "<u>sunny</u> morning", "<u>frosty</u> lawn".
adverb	A word that <u>describes</u> a <u>verb</u>, e.g. "She sang <u>loudly</u>."
alliteration	The <u>repetition</u> of a <u>sound</u> at the beginning of words within a phrase, e.g. "<u>L</u>oopy <u>L</u>ois <u>l</u>ikes <u>l</u>ipstick."
antonym	A word with the <u>opposite meaning</u> to another word, e.g. "on" and "off".
collective noun	A name for a <u>group</u> of things, e.g. "a <u>flock</u> of sheep".
fiction	Text that has been <u>made up</u> by the author, about <u>imaginary people</u> and <u>events</u>.
homophones	Words that <u>sound the same</u>, but mean different things, e.g. "<u>hair</u>" and "<u>hare</u>".
imagery	Language that creates a <u>vivid picture</u> in the reader's mind.
metaphor	A way of <u>describing</u> something by saying that it <u>is</u> something else, e.g. "Mr Smith was an angry dragon."
non-fiction	Text that is about facts and <u>real people</u> and <u>events</u>.
noun	A word that <u>names</u> something, e.g. "<u>scissors</u>", "<u>chair</u>".
onomatopoeia	When words <u>sound</u> like the <u>noise</u> they describe, e.g. "<u>pop</u>", "<u>bang</u>".
phrase	A <u>part of a sentence without a verb</u> which doesn't make sense on its own, e.g. "the purple dress".
plural	<u>More than one</u> of something, e.g. "birds".
prefix	A letter or letters that can be <u>added to the start</u> of a word to <u>change its meaning</u>, e.g. "<u>un</u>lock".
pronoun	Words that can be used <u>instead</u> of <u>nouns</u>, e.g. "<u>I</u>", "<u>you</u>", "<u>he</u>", "<u>it</u>".
proper noun	A <u>name</u> for a <u>particular place</u>, <u>thing</u> or <u>person</u>, e.g. "<u>James</u>", "<u>Paris</u>".
simile	A way of describing something by <u>comparing</u> it to something else, e.g. "The stars were <u>like</u> a thousand diamonds."
suffix	A letter or letters that can be <u>added to the end of a word</u> to <u>change its meaning</u>, e.g. "use<u>ful</u>".
synonym	A word with a <u>similar meaning</u> to another word, e.g. "<u>big</u>" and "<u>huge</u>".
verb	An <u>action</u> or <u>being</u> word, e.g. "I <u>run</u>", "he <u>went</u>", "we <u>think</u>".

F4OF1